Banwell Volunteer Fire Unit, Avon, using a manual fire engine purchased by the churchwardens of Banwell in 1810 for £40 7s. It was made by Ester Manley of Redcliffe Hill, Bristol, and pumps 44 gallons (200 litres) of water per minute to a height of 80 feet (24 metres).

FIREFIGHTING EQUIPMENT

Brian Wright

Shire Publications Ltd

CONTENTS

Printed in Great Britain by C. I. Thomas & Sons (Haverfordwest) Ltd, Press Buildings, Merlins Bridge, Haverfordwest, Dyfed.

British Library Cataloguing in Publication Data available.

ACKNOWLEDGEMENTS

The author wishes to thank the late Sid Brown, London Fire Brigade Museum, Southwark; Ron Long; Michael Lovegrove of the Chartered Insurance Institute; the Trustees of the Museum of Fire and Firefighting Trust; Peter Rigarlsford; Brian Sharp; Sheree Thurston of the Norwich Union Insurance Group; the Mistress of Girton College, Cambridge; Jean West for passing on much valuable information; and Valerie Wright for patiently reading the manuscript and making many helpful suggestions.

Cover: *Part of a lithograph published about 1825 entitled 'London Fire Engines, The Noble Protectors of Lives and Property'. In the foreground the watchman raises the alarm with his rattle while a large fire engine of the County Fire Office races towards the fire. The turncock, assisted by a fireman, is turning on the water to supply the engines, while the parish fire engine, under the direction of the beadle, is pulled along the pavement. The sense of drama and urgency is clearly conveyed in this illustration.*

Below: *The frontispiece of 'Wofull News from the West-parts of England', printed in 1598, showing a fire hook and buckets of water being used to fight a fire which caused major damage at Tiverton, Devon, in that year.*

A hose cart made by Sarah Dixon and Son. This is the 'West Lea' model and contains hose, extinguishers, stand pipes and other firefighting equipment and would have been used to tackle small fires by the fire brigade. They were kept in industrial premises and large country houses and were made by a number of makers between the 1860s and the 1930s.

THE FIRST FIRE ENGINES

Fire has been a particular danger since houses began to be built close together to form towns and cities, especially where buildings were made mainly of timber, when a fire could spread quickly from one to another. The Romans recognised this hazard and organised groups of slaves into a fire brigade to protect the city of Rome as early as 6 BC.

Following a reorganisation of this brigade in the first century AD, others were formed at various places in the Empire, including Britain, although some rich Roman householders did not rely on the city fire brigade but employed men as a private brigade to protect their property and goods.

The Roman fire brigade had a wide range of equipment including a manually operated double-cylinder force pump, used as a fire engine. This was based on a design of pump invented by Ctesibius, an Alexandrian who lived in the second century BC, which was capable of producing a continuous jet of water. The three examples of surviving Roman fire engines, one of which was found in Britain, are a simpler version of this and could produce only an intermittent jet, but more sophisticated pumps are described by Roman writers.

Following the end of Roman rule in Britain around AD 410, organised firefighting was to disappear for a long time. From the Saxon period through to the end of the seventeenth century chaos frequently reigned at fires, which were a regular occurrence, and the same town was often burnt time after time. It is not surprising that outbreaks of fire were so

A couvre feu used to cover domestic fires when the curfew bell was rung, as it was realised very early on that the majority of fires break out at night. They are usually made of iron, although a few brass examples are known.

common since, until recently, open fires were used for cooking and heating, while many hazardous industrial processes were carried out in close proximity to houses. Candles, rush lights, oil lamps and, more recently, gas were used for lighting, all providing further potential sources of fire.

Numerous rules and regulations have been passed over the centuries concerning precautions to take against fire and the provision of firefighting equipment, and many of these would have directly concerned householders. One of the earliest was a law passed at Oxford by King Alfred in AD 872 which required all fires to be covered at night when a bell was rung. This was extended to the whole of England following the Norman invasion. To damp down the fire and ensure the embers did not re-ignite, a metal cover, known as a *couvre feu*, was placed over it and it is from these Norman-French words that the English term 'curfew' is derived.

In 1189 the first Lord Mayor of London, Henry Fitz-Alwin, passed regulations requiring the occupants of larger houses in the city to keep a ladder ready to help their neighbours escape from a fire, and between Whit Sunday and 24th August they had to keep a barrel of water by their front doors. Firefighting equipment was very basic during the medieval period and consisted mainly of buckets and fire hooks, but later they did have large syringe-like pumps known as squirts. These were introduced into Britain from Europe about 1600 and continued in use until the eighteenth century.

Fire engines introduced in Augsburg, Germany, in 1518 are described as 'instruments for fires' or 'water syringes', which suggests that they were only squirts; as, however, they incorporated wheels and levers they were obviously more sophisticated. In 1548 a German visitor to London saw a fire engine at the head of the Lord Mayor's procession where it was being used to throw water on to the crowd to clear the way, but nothing further is known of this machine.

The earliest detailed description of a force pump is found in a work written by Heinrich Zeising in 1612 and, like all these early fire engines, it was mounted on a sled rather than wheels. The water had to be poured into its cistern using buckets and the jet of water came from a swivelling nozzle mounted on the machine. A few years later, in 1615, Salomon de Caus described and illustrated a fire engine which was able to throw a jet of water to a height of 40 feet (12 metres). It was in widespread use in Germany, where many different forms of fire engine were being developed in the first quarter of the seventeenth century.

In 1625 the first English fire engine patent was granted by James I to Roger Jones whose design was based on pumps he and his brother had seen in Nuremburg, an example of which they apparently brought back. They had two machines under construction by William Burroughs when Roger Jones died in the plague of 1625-6. Burroughs continued to build and modify them and by 1660 had made about sixty.

In his book published in 1634 John Bate shows several types of fire engine,

4

The earliest illustration of a squirt appears in 'De Re Metallica' published around the middle of the sixteenth century. This shows a smelting works with a fire point against one wall consisting of buckets, fire hooks, sledge hammer and squirt all contained in a special rack. This indicates that at least some owners of early industrial premises were aware of the dangers of fire.

An eighteenth-century brass squirt with a wooden handle. The side handles were held by two men who directed the jet while a third pushed in the wooden handle to expel the water. It was more efficient than a bucket of water as the jet could be directed at the seat of the fire.

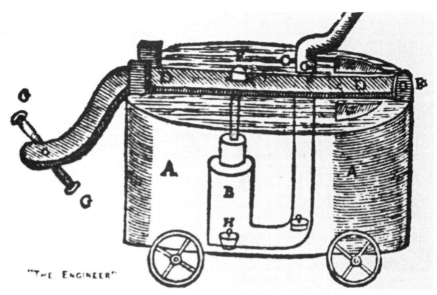

One of seven different types of fire engine illustrated by John Bate in 'A Treatise on Art and Nature', published in 1634. He describes these as 'engines to be drawn upon wheeles from place to place, for to quench fier among buildings; the use whereof hath been found very commodious and profitable in cities and great townes'.

Another of the engines illustrated by John Bate in 1634, which clearly shows the valves it incorporated.

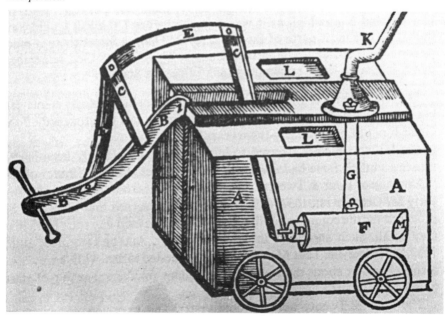

A single-cylinder manual fire engine as described by Salomon de Caus in his book 'Forcible Movements' published in 1615. This was mounted on a sled and pulled over the cobbles but could easily have been placed on a wagon for transportation.

and over the next three decades they were not only imported from Germany but were being built in England by several makers. They were bought by parishes for public use, by the royal dockyards and other royal establishments and, since they could be used for other general water pumping duties, were probably in the possession of a few private individuals.

When the Great Fire of London occurred in 1666 there were a number of fire engines available, but a conflagration on this scale was totally beyond the capabilities of these simple pumps and they made little contribution to the firefighting. This disaster emphasised the very real danger of fire, and between 1670 and 1690 a number of innovations, mostly intro-

duced from abroad, greatly improved the efficiency of fire engines. By this period most were fitted with wheels. In 1674 delivery hose was used in England following its invention in Amsterdam two years earlier, which allowed water to be taken to the seat of a fire. The *Philosophical Transactions* of the Royal Society of London, 1676, describe fire engines with an air vessel. This was a major advance since it enabled a continuous jet of water to be produced instead of an intermittent one.

In 1690 John Lofting patented a fire engine almost identical to those in use in Amsterdam. Like the Dutch engines, this had a wired suction hose which could draw water directly into it, so dispensing with the bucket chain to fill the cistern.

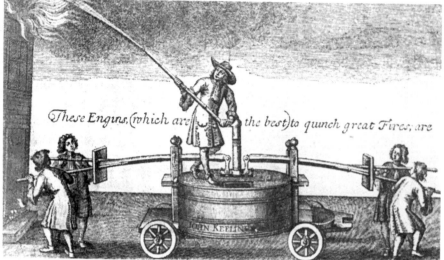

A fire engine made in the 1670s by John Keeling of Blackfriars, London. Unlike other manual pumps, the levers on both sides were on up and down strokes together. The only surviving example is in the Museum of London and was supplied to the town of Dunstable, Bedfordshire, in 1678. Unfortunately it is incomplete.

The introduction of the air vessel was a major advance in fire engine design. As the piston (A) is raised, water from the cistern is sucked into the cylinder through valve B. When the piston is pushed down the pressure closes valve B and opens valve C. The water is pushed into the air vessel where it compresses the air at the top of the vessel (D). The compressed air pushes down on the water, closing valve C and driving the water up tube E and out through the nozzle. This enables the pump to produce a jet of water even when the cylinder is being refilled (as shown in the diagram).

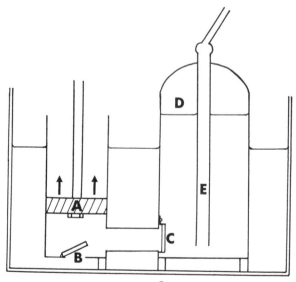

A manual fire engine probably made by Richard or Lawrence Newsham between 1725 and 1765. It incorporates foot treadles as well as hand levers and, although not the largest they built, was still capable of pumping between 90 and 120 gallons (409 and 545 litres) per minute.

ADVANCES IN DESIGN

There were a number of manufacturers producing fire engines of various designs by the early eighteenth century, but no major advance in fire engine technology occurred until 1725. In that year Richard Newsham was granted a patent for a new type of fire engine, which was to remain in production for almost a hundred years. Newsham realised that the more men who could work the engine, the greater the jet of water that could be produced; he therefore placed the pumping levers along the sides of the machine instead of at the ends. To gain additional power, he provided foot treadles on which men stood, shifting their weight from side to side, thus assisting those pumping by hand.

Water was either poured into the engine's cistern using buckets or taken in by a suction hose directly from a water source. Some contemporary illustrations show the jet of water coming from a swivelling goose-neck nozzle on top of the engine, but in many cases this was replaced by a length of leather delivery hose which enabled the water to be taken to the seat of the fire. Newsham's engines were produced in six sizes, the largest of which could project 170 gallons (772 litres) per minute a distance of 40 yards (38 metres).

These engines were very popular and were soon in use all over Britain by insurance company fire brigades, some parishes, large country houses and at the

Left: *The mechanism of a Newsham fire engine. The tall air vessel can be seen behind the rocking bar from which hangs the flat link chain which is used to convert the rocking motion of pumping into an up and down movement of the pistons.*

Right: *A fireman of the Sun Fire Office holds a pole axe in one hand and a lighted link, made of pitch and tow, in the other. Behind him a Newsham fire engine is being pumped by use of hand levers and foot treadles. This illustration was published in 1808.*

royal palaces. A writer in *The London Magazine* of 1752 considered that Richard Newsham's invention gave 'a nobler present to his Country than if he had added provinces to Great Britain'. Newsham-style fire engines continued to be produced by a number of makers until about 1820 and were still in use well beyond that, one example as late as 1940.

Despite the success of the Newsham-style engines, a number of eighteenth- and nineteenth-century makers were building manual pumps to less efficient designs, but which were technically easier to construct and probably cheaper to buy. An exception to this was the semi-rotary fire engine built by the prolific inventor Joseph Bramah which, despite being well made and quite efficient, does not seem to have sold in any great numbers.

The first decade of the nineteenth century saw the introduction of a new design of fire engine which, although broadly based on Newsham's principles, incorporated a number of changes. These engines were longer and wider than earlier machines and were all provided with springs, brakes, spoked wheels and a driver's seat. Along their sides they had pumping levers which were usually considerably longer than the engine and had hinged sections at each end so they could be folded up for travelling.

The engines were soon adopted by the insurance company brigades and later by some parishes and the volunteer and municipal brigades which were formed from the 1850s onwards. They were also purchased by many country house owners to protect their own property and often

A manual fire engine with its pumping handles placed at the ends. The mechanism is simpler and less efficient than that used by Newsham and, later, John Bristow.

A fire engine, built by Samuel Phillips, which has the rear handles set across the machine, but at the front there is one on each side to prevent the pumpers falling over the drag handle.

A semi-rotary fire engine, made by Joseph Bramah, which was apparently quite effective but never became very popular. This dates to the second half of the eighteenth century. Similar machines were later built by Thomas Rowntree. Because of the prominent air vessel they earned the contemporary name of 'balloon engines'.

the surrounding villages, while others were provided for use in industrial premises of all types. These engines were produced in a variety of sizes ranging from those worked by twelve men up to the largest, which required 46 pumpers. They were subject to various technical improvements until, by the 1860s, they had become very efficient, and the design continued to be built and sold in quite large numbers until around 1914.

The next major advance in fire engine design was the introduction of steam power by Braithwaite and Ericsson in 1829 but, despite its obvious efficiency and advantages over manual engines, it was not taken up by any of the insurance fire brigades who provided the main fire protection in Britain at that time. Steam fire engines were very unpopular with many members of the general public who were afraid that the use of steam-powered fire engines would do away with

the need for volunteer pumpers, and therefore payment for pumping the engines. By 1835 the inventors had managed to sell only five and gave up producing them, and steam power was not to be used again on a fire engine until a hand-pumped floating fire engine operating on the Thames was converted in 1854. In 1858 Mr Shand patented a land steam fire engine and in the next two years considerable development took place so that, from the 1860s, a variety of steam fire engines was produced.

Although expensive initially, they proved efficient, reliable and economic and so began to replace the large manual engines. They were used by municipal, insurance and the wealthier volunteer and industrial brigades, and were also bought by a number of country house owners, particularly in the 1880s and 1890s, when firefighting had become a fashionable interest for many gentlemen.

A 'London Brigade' style manual engine of the type introduced around 1800. These remained very popular and sold in large numbers to many public and private brigades. They range in size from those pumped by 16 men up to those which required 46 men and which, at 45 strokes per minute, could pump 165 gallons (750 litres) of water per minute.

A Shand Mason 'Platform' fire engine made in 1873 and used at Breamore House, Hampshire. This type of pump was suitable for general purpose pumping in mines and factories and on estates, besides being used for firefighting.

A 'New Volunteer' horse-drawn steam fire engine made by Shand Mason and Company. This type was particularly popular with volunteer brigades and many were purchased for use on country estates and industrial premises.

They would captain their own estate brigades of uniformed firemen, the members coming from the house and estate staff; these brigades were often very well equipped with items such as wheeled escapes and hose carts.

Around 1900 Merryweather and Sons introduced the self-propelled steam fire engine and, although most of these were purchased by municipal authorities, a few were used by private brigades.

The first petrol-driven fire pump, although still horse-drawn, was brought to Britain from Germany in 1895 by the owner of a large country house at Dat-chet, Berkshire. However, although it could be prepared for action in one minute, it produced a jet equivalent only to that of a six-man manual. The first self-propelled motor fire engine was built by Merryweathers in 1903, and within a few years the idea of the motorised fire engine had become accepted by many types of brigade, although few country estates acquired one. They rapidly began to supersede the manual and steam engines and, with further development and refinement, became the forerunners of today's highly efficient appliances.

A Merryweather 'Fire King' self-propelled steam fire engine used by the Norwich Union Fire Insurance Society at Worcester from 1905. These had a top speed of 30 mph (48 km/h) and were available with either coal- or oil-burning furnace. They were first introduced in 1899 and the last one was built in 1918.

A manoeuvrable light-weight appliance based on the Land-Rover. There are many variations in body and pumps made by a number of firms and these machines are used by many rural brigades, airports and industrial fire brigades. This example is towing a trailer pump which was produced in great numbers during the Second World War and into the 1950s.

A 1955 Bedford SB Special, provided with a Number 2 Dennis pump and a 35 foot (10.6 metre) Bailey ladder. Only 27 of this type were built and this example served at the Fort Dunlop Tyre Factory in Birmingham until 1981.

A small hand pump supplied to the Birmingham Fire Office in the early nineteenth century. This has a single pumping-lever and piston and was intended to be used to tackle fires in their early stages.

In 1879 the girls of Girton College, Cambridge, decided to form their own fire brigade as the local brigade might take too long to reach them if a fire occurred. In this photograph, taken in 1886, a number of items of firefighting equipment can be seen, including fire grenades, ratchet warning rattle, canvas buckets and a corridor engine. The college maintained its own brigade until the 1930s.

DOMESTIC FIRE PUMPS

The smallest of the eighteenth-century fire engines easily fitted through doorways and so it was possible to use them inside buildings. A few examples seem to have been made mainly for use in large houses or factories. However, it was the following century that saw a proliferation of small fire engines and hand pumps specifically designed for dealing with a fire in the early stages before it spread out of control. It was important for houses to keep their own firefighting equipment: well into the twentieth century many fire brigades were made up of part-time volunteers, often using horse-drawn fire engines, so it could take longer for the brigade to reach the scene of a fire than today.

One of the earliest of these small fire engines was built by Mr Hornblower in 1807 and consisted of a pump in a box 14 inches (35 cm) high which was kept filled with water and placed in a convenient position in the house. Around 1835 Bramah and Robinson produced 'The Swiss Portable Fire Engine', which was a pump in a wooden bucket made to be carried on the back and worked by one or two men. This could project 20 gallons (91 litres) of water a distance of nearly 70 feet (21 metres).

It was from the 1860s that Merryweather and Sons and Shand Mason and Company, the two largest fire engine manufacturers, began to produce a range of small pumps, all of which produced a

A corridor fire engine made by Shand Mason and Company between 1860 and 1890. Large buildings often had one of these filled with water on each floor. They have a fold-down carrying handle to enable them to be carried up and down stairs but are extremely heavy when full.

The Edwardian lady was expected to tackle a fire if she should encounter one; with this in mind the fire equipment makers produced items specifically for female use. The 'Ladies Boudoir Hand Pump' came with two special light-weight metal fire buckets with leather handles and was completed by a special painted or polished wood stand.

18

Left: *A late nineteenth- or early twentieth-century 'Tozer' pump, made by Shand Mason and Company. This was supplied with 10 feet (3 metres) of leather hose and when worked by two men was capable of throwing a jet of water to a height of 45 feet (13.8 metres).*

Right: *Small hand pumps of many types were bought in large numbers for use by fire brigades and in industrial premises, institutions and large houses. The manufacturers produced long lists of prestigious customers who had purchased one model or another.*

continuous stream of water. These were specially designed for use in larger houses and hotels, where the risks from using open fires, oil lamps and candles were greater than in the normal household. They were also bought for use in schools, factories and other large buildings.

The wheeled fire pumps were called corridor engines since they were kept in a convenient spot in the corridor, one on each floor, and consisted of a pump placed in a galvanised iron cistern of 15 to 20 gallons (68 to 91 litres) capacity. They were kept filled with water ready for instant use if a fire broke out and were provided with a length of hose to direct the jet of water.

Corridor pumps were relatively inexpensive, ranging from basic models cost-ing around £6 18s for a machine capable of projecting between 8 and 15 gallons (36 and 68 litres) per minute a distance of 50 feet (16 metres), up to the most expensive and sophisticated examples costing £15 and throwing 25 gallons (113 litres) per minute to a height of 50 feet (16 metres). They came in a standard bright red finish with black, white or gold lining but could also be supplied in colours to match the client's décor or with coats of arms, monograms or suitable inscriptions.

The companies published some glow-ing testimonials for these devices from members of the aristocracy, captains of fire brigades and others who had used them to save property. Lists of customers were also produced which show that they

Left: A 'London Brigade' pump by Shand Mason and Company. Although six hundred were in use by the London Fire Brigade, a great many others were supplied to other brigades, large houses, hospitals, museums and so on. This was one of the most popular of the domestic fire pumps and cost £3 7s 6d in 1906.

Right: A stirrup pump designed to meet the dangers of incendiary bombs in the Second World War. It is very simple in having only three moving parts but is efficient and easily maintained. It was supplied with 30 feet (9 metres) of rubber hose. The first models had a nozzle with a sliding mechanism to give a spray or a jet, but later versions gave a jet only.

were bought not only for private houses but also for theatres, schools, hospitals and other institutions and that they were installed at the royal palaces by Queen Victoria. Corridor engines were purchased in bulk by the Prince of Wales as gifts for Indian maharajas, which further boosted sales both in Britain and abroad. In the 1890s a number of different versions were available with such refinements as rubber tyres (at 25 shillings extra) and copper cisterns. They continued to be made into the 1930s and possibly later.

The bucket pump was also immensely popular during the second half of the nineteenth century, although its origins are much older. Sometime before 1844 William Baddely made an efficient hand pump somewhat like the ancient squirt but which had valves and an air vessel so that, when immersed in water, it could produce a continuous stream. By the 1850s a similar device was carried on each fire engine of the London Fire Brigade for use in the first stages of a fire and in

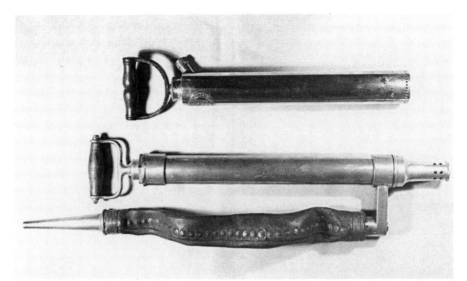

Two brass hand pumps. The upper is made by Merryweather and Sons and is similar to that designed by James Braidwood in 1848. It can throw a continuous jet of water a distance of 30 feet (9 metres). The lower pump incorporates a length of riveted hose and dates to the early years of the twentieth century.

A pair of glass fire grenades in their original wire basket. The Harden Number 1 grenade was patented by H. D. Harden of Chicago in 1871 and was sold in Britain by the Harden Star, Lewis and Sinclair Company Limited of Peckham, London.

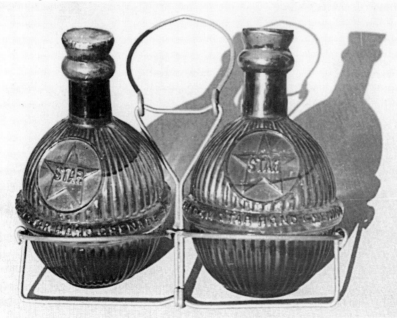

such places as warehouses, where the use of water had to be kept to a minimum to avoid damaging goods.

Alfred Tozer, Chief Officer of Manchester Fire Brigade, took out a patent in 1864 for a pump fixed in a bucket or cistern and this basic design was soon available in a wide range of styles from both Merryweather and Sons and Shand Mason and Company. Like the corridor engines they were often supplied with coats of arms or monograms. They came in a variety of sizes, usually with 10 feet (2.7 metres) of hose, the largest of which could pump a jet of water up to 40 feet (12 metres) high at a rate of 12 gallons (54 litres) per minute and, depending on the exact model, ranged in price from 6 to 10 pounds. They sold in vast numbers to many types of customer, domestic and institutional, as well as to fire brigades. Captain Shaw, head of the London Fire Brigade, claimed that of the 4199 fires which occurred in 1878 at least 2500 were extinguished by the use of these small pumps. Alfred Tozer, its inventor, pointed out in the 1880s that one pump in use at Manchester for 21 years had saved property to the value of £100,000. Bucket pumps continued to be manufactured into the 1930s.

The basic pump, without the cistern and with the addition of foot brackets and an intake hose, was also available in the 1880s and was suitable for a variety of domestic purposes such as gardening and window cleaning as well as firefighting. In the Second World War the stirrup pump was produced in large numbers, mainly to combat fires caused by incendiary bombs. They were issued to firefighters and fire watchers, placed in public and other large buildings, and bought by private householders.

Left: *The original fire extinguisher invented by Captain George Manby (1765-1854), which used compressed air to expel the extinguishing liquid.*

Right: *L'Extincteur extinguisher by W. Dick and Company of London. This was the forerunner of today's soda-acid extinguisher.*

(Left) Copper 'Tetclo' extinguisher, made by Siebe Gorman, which incorporates a hand pump. (Centre) An 'Empire' soda-acid extinguisher made by John Kerr and Company, Northwich, Cheshire. (Right) A soda-acid extinguisher made by William Miller of Glasgow in 1938. This has a hammer on the side which is used to shatter the phial of acid.

FIRE EXTINGUISHERS

What makes a fire extinguisher different from a hand pump or a fire grenade? Fire extinguishers are vessels which contain water or some other chemical which is expelled by pressure either stored within the extinguisher itself or generated by a chemical reaction.

The development of extinguishers got off to an explosive start, reflecting their mode of operation. Zachary Greyl in 1722, Ambrose Godfrey in 1723 and Charles Povey the following year all developed similar devices, the best of which was probably Godfrey's. This consisted of a sealed wooden barrel of water with chemical additives in a wickerwork basket. On top was a lined tin cover protecting a fuse which led down a tube

to a round pewter bomb containing a quantity of gunpowder. When a fire broke out, the fuse was lit and the extinguisher thrown into the burning room where it exploded and drenched the room with water so, theoretically, extinguishing the flames. Such devices were still in use in the 1760s.

The second half of the eighteenth century saw many recommendations for various chemicals to be added to the water used for fighting fires, and many demonstrations were staged. In practice, few, if any, would have made a difference to the extinguishing properties of water, despite their inventors' claims.

Although not strictly extinguishers, glass fire grenades made their appearance

23

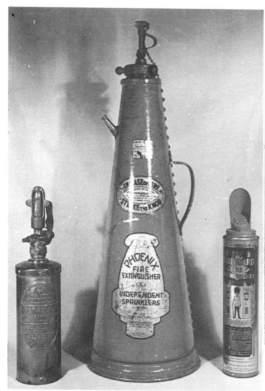

Left: *(From left to right) A 'Petrolex' extinguisher by Read and Campbell of Westminster, London, 1920, which uses a carbon dioxide cartridge to expel its contents; a conical soda-acid extinguisher by Independent Sprinklers Limited of Kingsway, London, 1941; the 'Safeguard Fire Extinguisher' made by the Fire Protection Company of Enfield, Middlesex, in the 1950s or 1960s. Water was added to a special chemical and, for use, the contents were shaken vigorously at the flames.*

Right: *A fire extinguisher cut away to show the gas cartridge from which the propelling gas is produced and the tube up which the water is forced.*

in the United States of America in 1871 and consisted of a sealed glass vessel of 1 or 1½ pints (570 or 855 ml) capacity, usually filled with a solution of sodium bicarbonate or simply brine or salt water. They were made in Britain from 1877 and can be found in a wide range of styles, many with ribs or other features to enable them to shatter easily when thrown at a fire. Many extravagant claims for their effectiveness were made by their various makers but, despite being extremely popular for about forty years, they were of little use in fire-fighting. James Merryweather, a manufacturer of firefighting equipment,

criticised them on their introduction, but such was the public demand that his firm started to produce them from 1895, and fire grenades continued to be produced until well into the twentieth century. Between 1900 and 1940 vaporising liquid grenades were produced along with glass vessels whose chemical contents had to be sprinkled on the flames.

The first true extinguisher was invented by George Manby in 1816 and was intended to be carried on a hand cart. It consisted of a copper vessel containing 3 gallons (13.6 litres) of pearl-ash (potassium carbonate), a chemical used for fire fighting since the eighteenth century.

A quarter of the extinguisher contained compressed air so that, when a tap was opened, the liquid was forced up a tube, which reached nearly to the bottom of the container, and out through the nozzle.

The late nineteenth and early twentieth centuries saw a number of extinguishers produced which incorporated a hand pump to create the pressure to expel the water in a continuous stream when a tap was opened. More recently, other gases as well as compressed air have been stored in extinguishers and used to expel the contents, while other types relied on a chemical reaction to propel the extinguishing medium. Phillips Patent Fire Annihilator of 1841 underwent a complex series of chemical reactions after a glass phial of sulphuric acid was broken. This produced considerable heat which drove water up tubes where it was heated, converted to steam and expelled as a cloud of water vapour.

Some extinguishers contained a mixture of acid and alkaline chemicals which reacted with each other to produce car-

(Left) CTC extinguisher made in 1954 by Minimax Ltd, Feltham, Middlesex. This type was mainly used in motor vehicles. (Centre) Dry powder extinguisher, 1950s, by Kyl Fyre Ltd, Eastbourne, East Sussex. (Right) A pistol fire extinguisher made by Antifyre Ltd, Acton, London. This type was patented by H. Hutchinson in 1930. The striker is cocked, the pistol aimed at the flames and the trigger pulled, firing a cloud of fire-extinguishing powder.

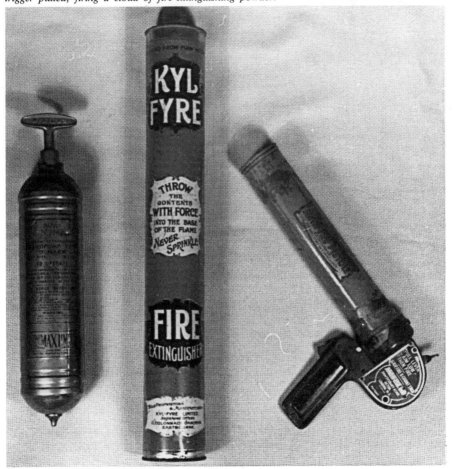

(Left) A glass extinguisher made by Stone and Company, Leytonstone, London. The top was broken and the contents sprinkled on the flames. (Centre) A glass grenade with, below it, two sulphuric acid phials for soda-acid extinguishers, the upper 1960s, and the lower 1930s. (Right) An extinguisher by the Fire Preventures Company, Reigate, Surrey, with its wall holder. In case of need the tube was removed from the holder, the lead seal on the nozzle broken and the tube squeezed to expel its contents at flames. According to the instructions, 'the fire would be instantly extinguished'.

bon dioxide gas, which kept the contents under pressure so they were expelled when a tap was opened. However, these were prone to leak gas and so might fail to work when required. In 1875 Dick's Patent Fire Exterminator was improved by having a sealed glass phial of sulphuric acid suspended above a solution of sodium bicarbonate. By pushing in a metal pin, the acid bottle was broken and the acid mixed with the sodium bicarbonate and produced carbon dioxide gas, which expelled the solution. This, with further improvements such as a strainer to prevent broken glass blocking the nozzle, is the basis of the modern soda-acid extinguisher. Some earlier types had to be turned over to drop a lead weight on to the acid phial to break it and were used inverted. Other extinguishers in-

corporate a gas cartridge operated by a plunger which releases the gas and this in turn forces out the water. This method was developed in the 1920s.

A further development in the 1930s of the chemical reaction principle was the foam extinguisher. Sodium bicarbonate, with a stabiliser to strengthen the bubbles, and a solution of aluminium sulphate were mixed when required to form foam and carbon dioxide gas, which both filled the bubbles and forced the foam out of the extinguisher. Some versions contain a foam solution which is expelled by stored air or nitrogen gas under pressure or a cartridge of carbon dioxide gas, the bubbles being formed as the liquid is expelled through a special nozzle at high speed. The foam blankets the flames and extinguishes them by cutting off their

26

contact with air.

In 1912 the Pyrene Company produced a brass pump-type extinguisher containing carbon tetrachloride (CTC), which is ejected as a liquid but rapidly vaporises to form a heavy layer of gas which excludes oxygen and so prevents combustion continuing. The pump was designed to produce a continuous jet and was mainly intended for use on motor vehicles, but larger CTC extinguishers were produced in the 1950s. From the 1930s to the present day a number of different types of vaporising liquid extinguishers have been produced.

On a similar principle is the more recently introduced carbon dioxide extinguisher containing the gas as a liquid under pressure. When released, this rapidly turns back to a gas which blankets the flames and prevents combustion. The earlier versions were operated by striking a plunger, but now a lever device is used.

A number of types of dry powder extinguisher have been produced since the 1930s and usually consist of a formula based on sodium bicarbonate or ammonium phosphate. The powder is ejected by compressed air, stored gas or a gas cartridge. They work by interfering with the chemical chain reactions occurring in the flames.

BUCKETS AND OTHER EQUIPMENT

Buckets are among the earliest items of firefighting equipment and an illustrated manuscript of the fifteenth century shows them being used to fight a fire. Over the next two centuries numerous regulations were passed concerning the provision and maintenance of fire buckets. For example, in 1574 every householder in Win-

Left: *Some extinguishers come in very large sizes and require wheels to transport them. These are known as 'chemical engines' and both soda-acid and foam types are found in this form. Some of the larger carbon dioxide extinguishers are provided with a trolley.*

Right: *A leather fire bucket of the eighteenth century with sewn rim, foot ring and seams. This technique of making buckets was superseded by riveting.*

27

Left: *(Left) Fire bucket of the late seventeenth or early eighteenth century specifically designed for use in bucket chains. (Right): Eighteenth-century riveted bucket with a copper band reinforcing the rim. This type continued to be made well into the twentieth century.*

Right: *Detail from an early nineteenth-century leather fire bucket which bears the impressed stamp BRISTOW, a firm producing fire engines and other firefighting equipment from 1765.*

chester was required to keep a 'lethern bucket' available in case of fire and failure to do so resulted in a fine. London's Court of Common Council in 1575 ordered that buckets were to be kept in churches, and the cost was to be borne by the parishioners. The same year saw all the Cambridge colleges equipped with buckets, hooks and ladders.

Lack of a piped water supply often meant that a bucket chain had to be organised, and the usual method was to form two lines, one of men who passed the full buckets towards the fire, and the other of women and children who passed the empty buckets back for refilling. Fire buckets were kept not only by individuals and in the churches, but large country houses often had them in large numbers, as did mills and other industrial premises. The fire insurance companies supplied many buckets to their agents, parishes and local authorities for public use, since this not only encouraged firefighting but generated publicity and goodwill. Between 1730 and 1830 the Sun Fire Office alone ordered and distributed ten thousand fire buckets.

Until the mid nineteenth century most buckets were made of leather and were often produced by local saddle and harness makers, who would also repair them. Others were supplied by the larger fire engine manufacturers, at least one of which stamped its name on them, probably indicating that the firm had made them. Many buckets are painted with names, initials or coats of arms so they could be returned to their owners after the fire was extinguished, but, despite this, many were still mislaid.

Gradually, new materials were introduced, 'tin buckets' by 1807, canvas buckets by 1834, and from the 1860s cast iron, galvanised iron, gutta-percha and India rubber were also available, although up to this last period leather buckets predominated.

Despite showing much variation in size and shape, fire buckets are characterised by a strong handle and a deep foot ring which could be grasped firmly when throwing the water on to the flames. Special bucket racks were made in the nineteenth century, often of an ornamental but functional style. Sand buckets, often with a lid and made of metal, seem to have appeared in the late

(Left) Iron fire bucket, probably dating to the late nineteenth century. (Right) A 'light-weight' fire bucket made of galvanised iron with a leather handle bearing a name plate showing it to have been made by Merryweather and Sons.

Two large fire hooks at West Lavington, Wiltshire. These are the largest type and were used for pulling down thatch, burning timbers and even, on occasion, cottages. They are about 20 feet (6.1 metres) long.

An eighteenth-century leather fireman's helmet. It is lined with soft leather stuffed with horsehair and was the kind of protection available to men in some parishes and the early insurance company brigades.

A ratchet warning rattle, probably early nineteenth century. These were used by both the parish watch and early fire brigades to give a warning and summon help. They may also have been used on fire engines to clear the way before bells were introduced.

nineteenth century, and round-bottomed buckets, designed to be hung on a rack and unsuitable for any other purpose, were common from the 1920s. Leather buckets, which around 1910 cost 15 shillings, probably continued to be available for some years.

Another early item of firefighting equipment was variously known as a fire hook, fire crook or preventer. They were also used by the Romans, who called them *harpagnes,* and were in common use from the medieval period. They basically consist of an iron hook mounted on a wooden shaft and were used to unthatch houses near a fire to stop it spreading, to pull down burning roofing, timbers and thatch, and even, in the case of the very largest hooks, to demolish entire houses to create a fire break. This was a technique to prevent fire spreading which was still used occasionally in the late eighteenth century. Like buckets, the provision of fire hooks is regularly mentioned in rules and regulations, one of the earliest of which was passed in London in 1189. This required ten reputable men of the ward and ten aldermen to provide a strong 'crook of iron' together with two chains and two strong cords.

Those fire hooks designed for individual use were usually 10 to 12 feet (3 to 3.6 metres) long, but the largest have shafts about 25 feet (7.6 metres) long, while one Scottish example is 30 feet (9.1 metres) long and weighs 84 pounds (38 kg). Its great length was needed to reach the roofs and upper floors of the tall Edinburgh tenement buildings.

Some of the smaller fire hooks, and almost all the largest examples, have rings on them to which ropes or chains were attached so that additional men or even horses could be used to provide more pulling power. One sixteenth-century illustration of a very large fire hook shows it mounted on a wheeled framework, which would have made it much easier to manoeuvre.

During the eighteenth century fire hooks were supplied to the insurance brigades and insurance agents, while those for public use were placed in easily accessible positions, such as in the cathedral gateway at Canterbury in Kent, or at the Guildhall in Thaxted, Essex. There is a variety of designs, besides the simple hook, some of which incorporate a blade which was used to cut through the binding on thatched roofs. Large fire hooks were still used in Cambridgeshire and Derbyshire as late as the 1860s to pull down thatched cottages and burning hay stacks, and small versions, now known as ceiling hooks, are used by the fire brigade today.

As time went on the amount of fire-fighting equipment available not only increased but tended to become specialised, particularly for the full-time brigades which began to be established from the second half of the nineteenth century. Many volunteer brigades equipped themselves as well as they could afford. Victorian ingenuity provided householders with a great range of items to fight fires, as well as alarms and escapes, many of them well designed and finished.

With better communications and a faster response by the fire brigade, household firefighting equipment became less common after 1945 and many interesting items were consigned to the rubbish tip.

Pumpers' tokens of Banbury Volunteer Fire Brigade, Oxfordshire. When the fire was extinguished these metal discs, 1¼ inches (33 mm) in diameter, were given to the volunteers who had pumped the manual engines. They were able to exchange these the next day for payment, a system operated by many early brigades.

FURTHER READING

Blackstone, G. V. *A History of the British Fire Service.* Routledge and Kegan Paul, 1957.
Goodenough, Simon. *Fire! The Story of the Fire Engine.* Orbis Publishing, 1978.
Green-Hughes, Evan. *A History of Firefighting.* Moorland Publishing, 1979.
Hillier, Richard. *Ready and Willing.* PVFB, Fire Station, Bourges Boulevard, Peterborough, 1984.
Home Office. *Manual of Firemanship, Part One.* HMSO, 1943, reprinted and revised 1947, 1955, 1976, 1980.
Ingram, Arthur, and Bishop, Denis. *Fire Engines in Colour.* Blandford, 1973.
Ingram, Arthur. *A History of Fire Fighting and Equipment.* New English Library, 1978.
Miller, Denis. *A Source Book of Fire Engines.* Ward Lock, 1983.
Olyslager, Piet. *Fire Fighting Vehicles, 1840-1950.* Warne, 1972.
Paul, Tony. *The Story of the Fire Service.* Almark Publishing, 1975.
Science Museum. *Fire Fighting Appliances.* HMSO, 1969. (A catalogue of the collection.)
Vince, John. *Fire-marks.* Shire Publications, 1973.
Whitehead, Trevor. Fire Engines. Shire Publications, 1981.
Wright, Brian. *The British Fire Mark, 1680-1879.* Woodhead Faulkner, 1982.

PLACES TO VISIT

Many museums have one or two fire engines in their collections but few have a large amount of firefighting equipment. Such items as estate engines, fire grenades and fire buckets can still be seen in some historic houses, although attention is not always drawn to them. The following is a brief selection of museums and houses which between them contain a wide range of firefighting equipment.

Banbury Museum, 8 Horsefair, Banbury, Oxfordshire OX16 0AA. Telephone: 0295 59855.
Bridewell Museum of Local History, Bridewell Alley, Norwich, Norfolk NR2 1AQ. Telephone: 0603 611277.
Bristol Industrial Museum, Prince's Wharf, Prince Street, Bristol BS1 4RN. Telephone: 0272 299771.
Glasgow Museum of Transport, 25 Albert Drive, Glasgow G41 2PE. Telephone: 041-423 8000.
Gunnersbury Park Museum, Gunnersbury Park, London W3 8LQ. Telephone: 01-940 1612.
Ham House, Petersham, near Richmond, Surrey TW10 7RS. Telephone: 01-940 1950.
Lynn Museum, Old Market Street, King's Lynn, Norfolk PE30 1NL. Telephone: 0553 775001.
Museum of London, London Wall, London EC2Y 5HN. Telephone: 01-600 3699.
Museum of Science and Engineering, Blandford House, West Blandford Street, Newcastle upon Tyne NE1 4JA. Telephone: 091 2326789.
Salisbury and South Wiltshire Museum, The King's House, 65 The Close, Salisbury, Wiltshire SP1 2EN. Telephone: 0722 332151.
Science Museum, Exhibition Road, London SW7 2DD. Telephone: 01-938 8000.
Shaftesbury Local History Museum, Gold Hill, Shaftesbury, Dorset SP7 8JW. Telephone: 0747 2157 or 3426.
South Yorkshire Fire Service Museum, West Bar, Sheffield. Telephone: 0742 581833. (Limited opening.)
Tyrwhitt-Drake Museum of Carriages, Archbishop's Stables, Mill Street, Maidstone, Kent ME14 1LH. Telephone: 0622 54497.
York Castle Museum, Tower Street, York YO1 1RY. Telephone: 0904 653611.